24 EASY CLASSICAL
SOLOS FOR VIOLIN

BOOK 1

HARRY HUNT, JR., MFA

24 Easy Classical Solos for Violin: Book 1
Harry Hunt, Jr., MFA

Published by Harry Hunt, Jr.
Chicago, IL
harryhuntjr.com

ISBN: 978-1-954127-11-1 (Paperback)

Printed in the USA
First Edition

DEDICATION

Harry Simpson Hunt, Sr. was a noted Chicago jazz musician. As a gifted artist and teacher, he played all the instruments; however, the trumpet was his instrument of choice. His unique approach to playing was unprecedented as he tapped into and unlocked the talents of many upcoming, inspiring musicians. Everyone who knew him unanimously agreed that he breathed and ate music. Harry's brilliance as an instructor, along with the music he produced, will forever be appreciated by generations to come.

CONTENTS

HOT CROSS BUNS

Moderato

AU CLAIR DE LA LUNE

Andante

TWINKLE

SCARBOROUGH FAIR

CHORAL FANTASY

Beethoven

Allegro

OH SUSANNA

Foster

Allegro

9

MARRIAGE OF FIGARO

Mozart

Presto

LONG LONG AGO

Bayly

Andante

RONDEAU

Mouret

PIANO CONCERTO #3

Beethoven

Allegro

12

GERMAN DANCE

Mozart

THE HEAVENS ARE TELLING

Haydn

BOURREE (Water Music)

Handel

Vivace

MINUET

Bach

Moderato

CARNIVAL OF VENICE

Benedict

Allegretto

SONATINA #1

Beethoven

Moderato

SYMPHONY #7 (2nd)

Beethoven

Allegretto

SYMPHONY #7 (3rd)

Beethoven

19

LONDONDERRY AIR

Andante

LIGHTLY ROW

Moderato

LULLABY

Brahms

Andante

BLUE DANUBE

Strauss

Moderato

MINUET I

Bach

EINE KLEINE

Mozart

Allegro

24 EASY CLASSICAL VIOLIN SOLOS: BOOK 2

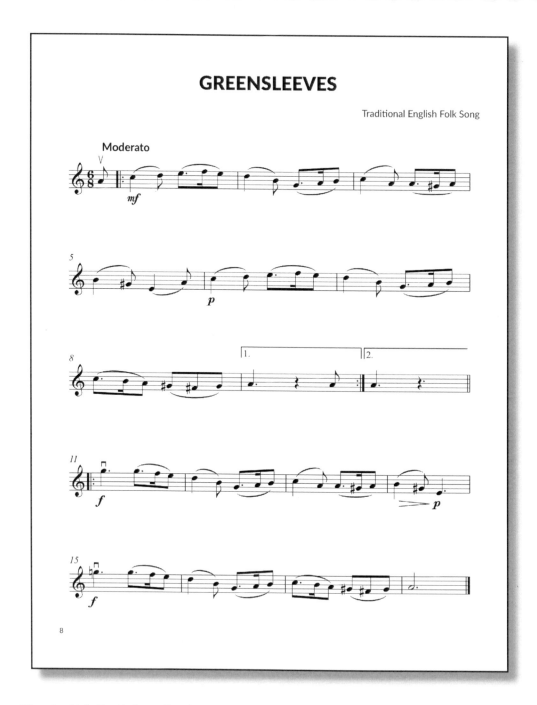

24 Easy Classical Violin Solos - Book 2 has short and simple pieces of some of your favorite classical melodies.

The music comes from classical composers such as: *Bach, Mozart, Beethoven, Mendelssohn, Vivaldi, Tchaikovsky and more.*

harryhuntjr.com/violin-bookstore